The Light

By Robert Jones

Healthy Life Press

The Light
Copyright © 2018 by Robert Jones

Published by:
Healthy Life Press
Bristol, Virginia

Text:
Robert Jones

Original photographs:
Robert Jones, (1, 4, 9, 11), Meiying Ng (2), Jessica Oliveira (3),
Arun Kuchibhotla (5), Juan Gomez (6), J.W. (7),
Juan Pablo Rodriguez (8), Levi Bare (10)

Digital Rendering:
Robert Jones

Most Healthy Life Press resources are available wherever books are sold.
Contact the publisher for volume pricing via healthylifepress.com.

For my girls

Why am I here?

To celebrate life.

Sometimes you will be reminded.

It may be that beauty stops you in your tracks.

It may be that the kindness of a helping hand
lifts you up.

Sometimes you must remember.

Our traditions across the world
and for every season
ask us to help one another
to pause
and create space.

In this openness,
we observe
the blessings of life
together.

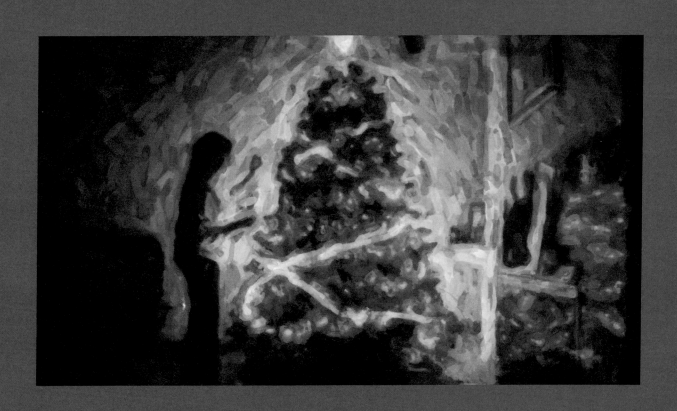

But storms come.

There are days of clouds
and there are days of sun.

Through it all, the Light shines.

Sometimes the Light will be called forth
from you.

It may be that you are moved to help.

It may be that you are moved to create.

Sometimes you must invite it.

It may be in prayer or meditation.

It may be alone or with others.

Whatever your path, the Light is within you
and all around you.

A note to parents ~

It is my sincere hope that this book serves in some small way
to help you and your child embark on a spiritual journey
together.

Reflections

Sometimes the Light will be called forth from you. In these moments, your worries and fears and your hopes and dreams fade. The world is sharply in focus and you act exactly as the situation requires. It is without effort from you; it is as if a great radiant energy is moving through you. It may be that you attend to someone suffering and that in a flow of limitless compassion, offer just the right silence and just the right words. It may be that you help bring something into the world - a flower or poem, perhaps. It won't be from your hands, but rather from an outpouring of nurturing love. However you experience this energy, it is always the same: you fall back and the Light shines forth.

Sometimes you must invite the Light. It is in the silence that arises when the expectations and judgment of your past experience stretch to meet the present moment, and then fall away. The energy of all that came before you is an ever-present force. The most fundamental choice in life is whether to be swept forward in that current, or to wade, wait, and ride. In that patience, time ceases, space expands, and that great radiant energy comes. When your body and mind are quiet and your heart is open, you well up with joy and infuse the world with it.

Lightning Source UK Ltd.
Milton Keynes UK
UKRC022021091019
351329UK00008B/183